M2/M3 BRADI

in action

by Jim Mesko

Color by Don Greer

Illustrated by Joe Sewell

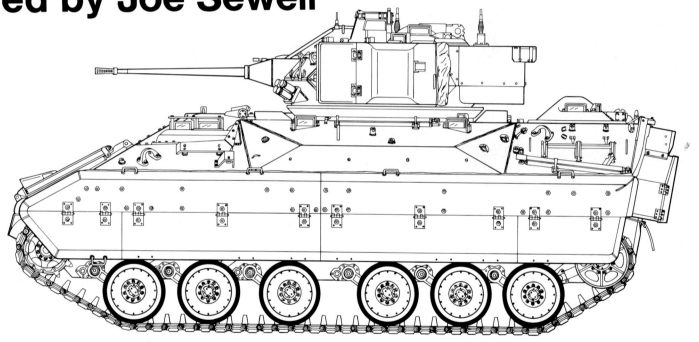

Armor Number 30

squadron/signal publications

HELLRAISER, an M3 Bradley of the 3rd Platoon, Alpha Troop, 4th Cav, 24th Mechanized Infantry Division rolls past a burned out Iraqi tank during Operation DESERT STORM.

ISBN 0-89747-280-2

If you have any photographs of the aircraft, armor, soldiers or ships of any nation, particularly wartime snapshots, why not share them with us and help make Squadron/Signal's books all the more interesting and complete in the future. Any photograph sent to us will be copied and the original returned. The donor will be fully credited for any photos used. Please send them to:

Squadron/Signal Publications, Inc.
1115 Crowley Drive.
Carrollton, TX 75011-5010.

Dedication

Dedicated to Mike Green, Michael Jerchel and Greg Stewart for all their help throughtout the years.

Acknowledgements

Mike Green
Greg Stewart
FT Knox Public Affairs Office
Patton Armor Museum
MAJ Richard Cole
U.S. Air Force
V. Roesner
Stephan Sewell
B. Zaeske
Stephanie Feagins

Michael Jerchel
FMC
Armor Magazine
COL Knox Bishop
U.S. Army
Oerlikon
Vought Industries
1/12 Cavalry
Egon Merk

An M2 of the 3rd Infantry Division (Mechanized) sits in a German field during a NATO exercise. The Bradley is a marked improvement over the M113 APC, which formed the backbone of armored and cavalry units for the last two decades. The M2/M3 gives these units a vehicle with a decided advantage over most light AFVs and the ability to mount a creditable defense against tanks. (FMC)

Introduction

When the tank first appeared on the battlefield during the First World War, it was hoped that this new weapon would break the stalemate of trench warfare on the Western Front. Unfortunately, the inability of the infantry to move forward quickly to consolidate the gains made by the tanks threw away the advantage this new weapon had given the Allies. Although some work had been done on armored vehicles to carry infantry forward alongside the tanks, the war ended before any significant steps were taken. Following the war, a lack of funds, conflicting tactical philosophies and political indifference stymied development of such vehicles in most countries.

The onset of the Second World War in September of 1939 saw the introduction of *BlitzKrieg* (Lightning War) by Germany, where fast moving tanks, supported by mechanized infantry, cut the Polish Army to pieces in just a few weeks. Within a year, using these same tactics, Germany conquered France and drove the British from the continent.

In the United States, Germany was viewed with apprehension and efforts were made to modernize the U.S. Army, particularly armored and mechanized units. Prior to the war, some work had been done on half-track vehicles. These vehicles had a tracked suspension replacing the rear wheels of a truck chassis. As a result of this work, the Army ordered into production the M2, and later, the M3 half-track for use by armored and mechanized units. These vehicles were fitted with light armor to protect their crews and infantry passengers from small arms fire and shell splinters, but lacked overhead protection. As a result of this shortcoming, they were used more as "battlefield taxies" than as assault vehicles. The infantry used these armored personnel carriers (APCs) to carry them forward with the armor. Once the objective was reached, the troops would disembark and attack on foot. While some attacks were carried out with the infantry onboard the armor, the lack of overhead cover made the infantry extremely vulnerable to small arms fire, shell bursts and hand-held weapons such as grenades.

As a result of the experience gained with the M2/M3, the Army began a series of experiments using the chassis of the M18 tank destroyer and M24 light tank in the APC role. Each vehicle, the M39 and M44, offered the advantage of being fully tracked, a definite improvement over the half-track concept, and the M44 had an armored roof. Both saw limited service, including action in Korea. These vehicles convinced Army planners that enclosed, fully tracked armored vehicles were needed for their new generation of APCs. After some discussion, the Army decided to develop a smaller version of the M44 design (based on the T43 tractor chassis) with better ballistic protection and an improved troop exit/entry capability.

Designated the M75, the vehicle went into service in 1952. While an improvement over the M44, the M75 was an expensive vehicle. It had a high profile, was not amphibious, and the engine cooling grills were susceptible to enemy fire.

These problems led the Army to seek a replacement vehicle even before the M75 went into full production. This came about when FMC offered the Army a privately designed APC which was smaller, lighter, less costly, and fully amphibious. In competition between the new design and a modified M75 (designated the T73), the FMC vehicle came out ahead and the Army decided to place this new vehicle, the M59, into production to supplement the M75. Within a relatively short period the M59 completely replaced the M75, most of which were either scrapped or given to the Belgium Army.

While the M59 was far superior to earlier designs, the Army was still not happy with its amphibious characteristics, engine arrangement and cross-country performance. They decided to have FMC develop a new APC which would form the basis for a whole family of related support vehicles. Two variants of the new vehicles were to be tested, one made of aluminum (designated T113) and the other made of steel (T117). After an intensive

The M113 was the result of experience gained with the earlier M75 and M59 along with new technology in the use of aluminum armor. One of the most successful post-Second World War AFVs, the M113 saw service around the world. In Vietnam, a large number of M113s were fitted with additional machine guns and shields under the designation ACAV. (Army)

The first U.S. attempt to develop an infantry fighting vehicle was the XM701 MICV-65. Due in part to its weight, slow speed and lack of air transportability, but also as a result of funding cuts brought about by the high cost of the Vietnam War, the XM701 was cancelled. (Army)

evaluation, the Army decided to procure the T113 since its aluminum construction offered similar protection for less weight when compared to the T117. Production began during 1959 under the designation M113 and this vehicle served as the basis for dozens of conversions by the U.S. and a host of other nations.

The M113 came into widespread use during the Vietnam war and the vehicle quickly proved to be effective and popular with the troops. Often it was used as an assault vehicle with the troops fighting from on top the vehicle rather than dismounting. To bolster its firepower and protection, two shielded mounts for M60 machine guns were fitted on either side of the troop hatch on the rear deck, and the commander's .50 caliber machine gun was also shielded. Vehicles with armor shields were called Armored Cavalry Assault Vehicles (ACAVs). While this improved the M113's firepower, the vehicle was still far from ideal as an armored assault vehicle. The most significant modification to improve its assault capabilities was the XM734 variant, which had firing ports added to the sides of the hull and rearranged the troops seats so that they faced outward. Although tested in Vietnam, this modification never became standard and the ACAV version became the main type used by infantry, armored, and mechanized units in Vietnam.

While generally satisfied with the M113, the Army began to look for a suitable replacement during the mid-1960s. The new vehicle was planned from the start to be used in the assault role as an Infantry Fighting Vehicle (IFV). This new vehicle, labeled the Mechanized Infantry Combat Vehicle - 1965 (MICV-65) was to have had firing ports to allow the troops to fire from inside the vehicle, be able to keep up with the proposed new main battle tank (MBT) and have armor protection against 14.5MM fire. From various designs submitted by a number of contractors, the Army choose the design submitted by Pacific Car and Foundry under the designation XM701. Unfortunately, the vehicle proved to be too heavy and slow and, coupled with the high cost of the Vietnam

FMC followed the XM765 with the XM800 which was aimed at replacing both the M114 and M551 as a cavalry scout vehicle. While a good, basic design the XM-800 was developed at a time when Congress was not in the mood to fund new armor projects and the Army cancelled it. As a result, it was decided to combine the scout and infantry vehicle requirements into one program. (Army)

War, these problems forced the Army to cancel the project. FMC, which had also submitted a proposal based on an extensively modified M113 (XM 765) was able to market the vehicle overseas to Belgium, Holland and the Philippines. These sales provided the company with valuable experience which was later to prove extremely beneficial.

Following the end of the Vietnam war, Army interest in the MICV began to surface once again in response to European and Russian advances in this type of armored vehicle. At the same time, the Army was also interested in a new Armored Reconnaissance Scout Vehicle (ARSV) to replace both the M114 and M551 Sheridan. FMC had designed a vehicle for this program, the XM800, which showed great promise, but the anti-military mood in Congress, coupled with a desire to cut back on defense costs, led to a reappraisal of the requirement. While work on the XM800 was progressing, FMC was also working on a new MICV, the XM 723, which somewhat resembled the XM765 although it was better protected and more powerful.

In 1975, recognizing Congressional opposition to military spending, the Army decided to merge the MICV and ARSV projects into one project to cut costs. A new set of criteria was issued, based on the needs of both the infantry and cavalry, using the XM723 as a starting point. The one-main turret, armed with a 20MM cannon, was replaced with a two man turret fitted with 25MM Bushmaster cannon. In addition, a pair of TOW missiles were fitted to the left side of the turret to give the vehicle an anti-tank capability to deal with Soviet MBTs. Because of its dual roles, the new vehicles had two different designations. The XM-2 Infantry Fighting Vehicles (IFV) or XM-3 Cavalry Fighting Vehicle (CFV); the X was dropped when the vehicle was accepted into service during 1980. Initially, it was planned to give each a different name, with the M2 being named after GEN Omar Bradley and the M3 after GEN Jacob Devers. In the event, due to the general similarity of both vehicles, they were both named the Bradley (shortened Bradley Fighting Vehicle - BFV).

After the demise of the XM701, FMC developed a heavily modified version of the M113 for the MICV program, designated the XM765. Armed with a 25MM cannon, the vehicle offered numerous advantages over the standard M113, but the Army decided against acquiring the vehicle. FMC was allowed to market it to foreign countries and it was purchased by Belgium, the Philippines and Holland (designated the YPR-765). (Jerchel)

Development

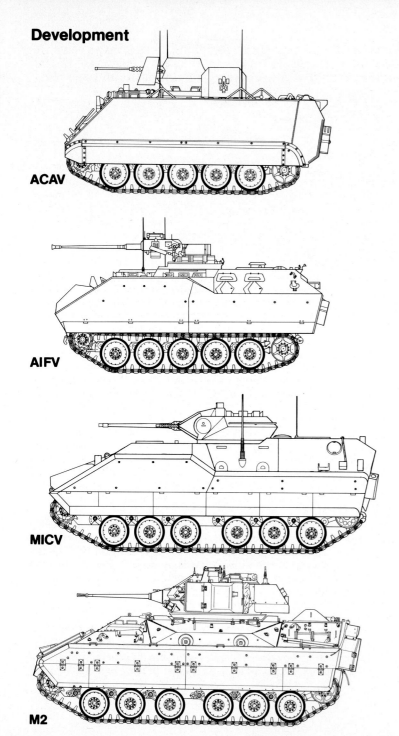

ACAV

AIFV

MICV

M2

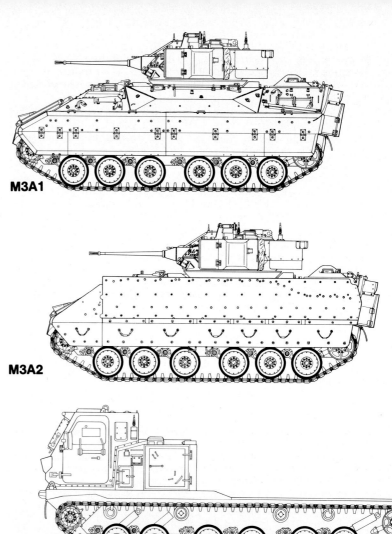

M3A1

M3A2

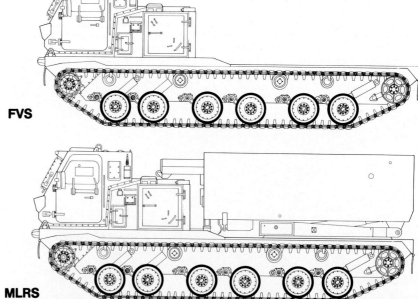

FVS

MLRS

M2/M3 Bradley

The M2/M3 Bradley was designed with the aid of considerable data from similar vehicles in both allied and Soviet service, including the West German Marder and the Russian BMP. Using this information, along with its own experience with the M113, XM734 and XM723, FMC developed a vehicle which could be used by both the infantry and cavalry without severely compromising either role.

Externally the M2 and M3 are almost identical. The main differences between them are the plating over of the fighting ports and the deletion of the hull periscopes on the right side of the M3. Like the earlier M113, the Bradley is made of welded aluminum armor and fitted with spaced, laminated armor plates around the hull. Power is provided by a 500 hp Cummins V.T.A. 903 T turbo-charged diesel engine which is mounted in the right side of the front hull. The power plant is coupled to a three speed General Electric HM PT-500 hydro-electric transmission. This combination of engine and transmission gives the M2/M3 rapid acceleration, agility and the ability to sustain high speeds for a prolonged period of time.

The top speed is near forty mph and the cruising range is some 265 miles when fully fueled (175 gallons). The torsion bar suspension system is composed of six rubber tired bogey wheels with hydraulic shock absorbers on the first, second, third and sixth wheels. The drive sprocket is located in the front with the idler wheel in the rear. Three track return rollers are mounted on the hull side, the first and third being single rollers, while the middle roller is a double unit. This suspension allows for an easy ride, good maneuverability and good handling characteristics.

The driver sits to the left of the engine in a fairly spacious driving compartment. He controls the Bradley using a simple steering yoke and peddles which were designed for ease of operation. The driver's compartment is fitted with a large hatch, with four vision periscopes, which opens up to the rear for easy access and exit. It can also be locked in the open position when not in a hostile environment. To help with night driving, the front, middle periscope can be fitted with a passive AN/VVS-2 night lens. A passageway connects the driver with the troop compartment. Along this tunnel are two firing positions (M2 variant) where squad members operate a modified M16A1, the M231, which is more compact than the M16 and fires only full automatic.

The turret is offset to the right of the tunnel. Constructed of aluminum and steel, the turret is fitted with a Hughes M242 25MM chain gun. Mounted coaxilly with the cannon (to the right) is an M240 7.62MM machine gun. The cannon can fire a variety of ammunition such as Armor Piercing Discarding Sabat-Tracer (APDS-T), High Explosive Incendiary-Tracer (HEI-T) and training rounds. The turret has a complete 360 degree electric traverse with an elevation range from plus 60 degrees to minus 10 degrees. The armament system is fully stabilized, allowing the Bradley to remain on target and fire while on the move. In addition to the cannon and machine gun, the M2/M3 is also fitted with an armored dual BGM-71 TOW missile launcher on the left side of the turret. When not in use, this armored launcher lies alongside the turret, but in action, it can be quickly elevated for use against any enemy AFVs which the cannon cannot destroy.

The system, designed by Hughes Aircraft, has an elevation of plus 30 degrees to minus 20 degrees and the missile has a range close to two miles. Once the missiles are fired, reloading is accomplished by elevating the launcher and tilting the end toward the rear crew hatch. A crewman then inserts fresh rounds from under the cover of the partially opened hatch. Overall control of the various armaments are exercised by the gunner and commander who are located in the turret, the gunner to the left and the commander to the right. Both have identical controls for operating the armament, periscopes for all-

Hull Development

M2 IFV

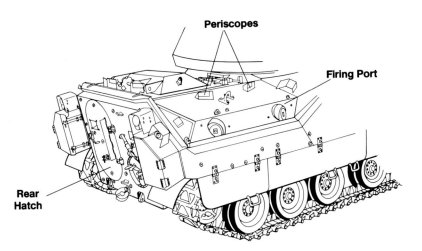

Periscopes

Firing Port

Rear Hatch

M3 CFV

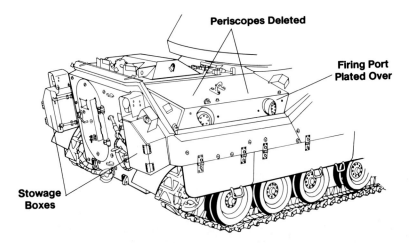

Periscopes Deleted

Firing Port Plated Over

Stowage Boxes

round vision, along with sighting devices for the weapons. These sights include both daylight and thermal imaging night systems, combined with what is known as a Integrated Sight Unit (ISU). This allows the Bradley to engage targets in clear weather, at night, or during smokey, dusty, or foggy conditions using the thermal sighting system. The commander also has the ability to observe terrain or targets from under the cover of his hatch which can be raised vertically over his head for protection against airbursts, small-arms fire, and shrapnel.

Behind the turret area is the troop compartment. Here is where the M2 and M3 radically differ. The M2 is configured to carry seven men who can fire out of the various firing ports located on the hull sides and rear ramp using the modified M16 rifles mounted in a ball-joint port. The troops acquire their targets through periscopes mounted above each firing ports. Basically this is "supression" fire, designed more to keep the enemy under cover, rather than to inflict any real casualties. The periscopes also allow the troops to be familiar with the terrain before they disembark, help relieve the feeling of helplessness soldiers experienced in the earlier APCs and cuts down on the feeling of claustrophobia. The troop compartment also carries additional 25MM ammunition, TOW rounds, small arms ammunition, personal gear, rations and water.

The main difference between the M2 and M3 troops compartments is that the M3 only carries two men, with most of the remaining space taken up by ammunition storage. This has resulted in some rearrangement of the storage racks and seats, but otherwise, the two vehicles are identical, save for the platedover side firing ports and the deletion of the periscopes over the right side ports.

Following the testing of eight prototypes during which no significant problems arose, the Army gave the go-ahead for production to start of the vehicle, now known as either the M2 Infantry Fighting Vehicle (IFV) or the M3 Cavalry Fighting Vehicle (CFV). The main external difference between the two variants was the plating over of the side firing ports and the deletion of the periscopes on the right side of the M3. (FMC)

This wooden mock-up of the M2 IFV revealed the major differences between the proposed version and the XM723, including a new two-man turret, redesigned hull and the addition of a pair of TOW anti-tank guided missiles in a retractable armored box alongside the turret. (FMC)

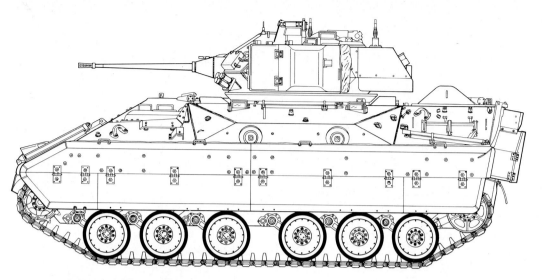

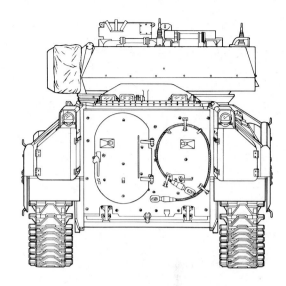

Specifications

M2 Bradley

Crew	Three
Length	21.5 feet
Width	10.5 feet
Height	9.75 feet
Weight	60,000 pounds

Armament

Main	25мм Bushmaster cannon
Secondary	7.62мм coaxial machine gun
	TOW missile launcher
Engine	500 hp Cummins VTA 903 Diesel
Speed	41 mph
Range	300 miles

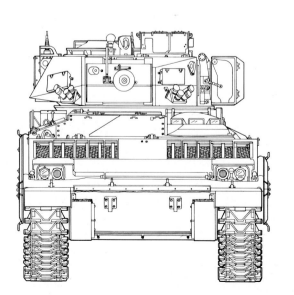

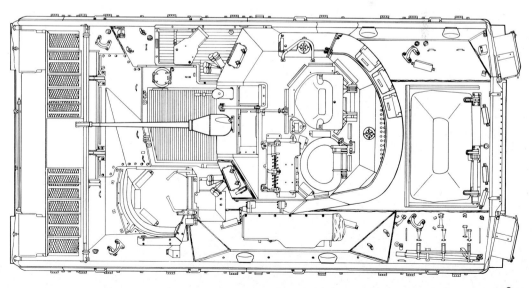

Production of the initial batch of M2/M3s began in 1980 at the FMC plant in California. The first contract called for 100 vehicles, split between 75 M2s and 25 M3s. Here work is being done on the turret. The large hole in the side is for the TOW launcher mechanism. (FMC)

Bradley hulls toward the end of the assembly process. The engines, on the right, are being prepared for installation in the hulls. The darker areas on the hull is where a non-skid surface has been applied. (FMC)

The all-round fire power potential of the Bradley is shown to good advantage in this factory shot of the lines of fire from the main gun and firing ports of the M2. The firing ports are equipped to handle a cut-down version of the M16 known as the M231 Firing Port Weapon (FPW). (FMC)

Normally, the rear ramp is let down so that the infantry can disembark as quickly as possible. (FMC)

Power for the Bradley comes from a Cummins VTA-903T 500 HP Diesel engine fitted in the forward right side of the hull. In this position it provides additional protection for the crew and ammunition which is stored in the compartment behind it. (Jerchel)

The trim vane folds down to serve as a work stand when maintenance is needed on the engine. This allows easy access to the engine compartment, thus lessening the amount of effort the crew must exert during maintenance periods in the field or at base. (Jerchel)

The driver is equipped with a large hatch fitted with four periscopes. The hatch may be locked in the up position when the situation allows and may be quickly pulled down using the handle shown on the right side of the hatch which has a strap attached to it. (Jerchel)

The infantrymen or scouts carried by the IFV or CFV variants can exit through the door in the rear of the hull on the rear ramp. Two firing ports are visible here, one on the door, and one inside the tow cable circle. (Jerchel)

11

The main aemament of the M2/M3 is the Hughes M242 25MM Bushmaster cannon. Secondary armament includes a 7.62MM machine gun mounted coaxially on the right side and a two tube TOW missile launcher. The primary gunner's sights are located in an armored box next to the TOW launcher. The sight between the cannon and machine gun is the commander's anti-aircraft sight for the main gun. (Jerchel)

The TOW launcher is raised and lowered through a lift mechanism located in an indented space in the turret side. When not in the firing position the armored missile launcher is retracted and lies flat alongside the turret. (Jerchel)

The Bradley has a potential anti-tank capability with the two tube TOW launcher mounted on the left side of the turret. The launcher is in the raised firing position with the armor cover down. The armored flaps of the gunner's sight is also raised, showing the glass covers. The one on the left is Blue while the other is Red. Smoke grenade launchers are located at the bottom of the turret while just above them is a stowage box for extra rounds. (Jerchel)

Rounds for the TOW launcher are loaded through the rear of the armored launcher box. The missiles are contained in a packing tube which is aligned with guide rails inside the launcher and inserted, packing tube and round, all at once. The missile launcher has a capacity for two TOW missiles with extra rounds being carried inside the vehicle. (Jerchel)

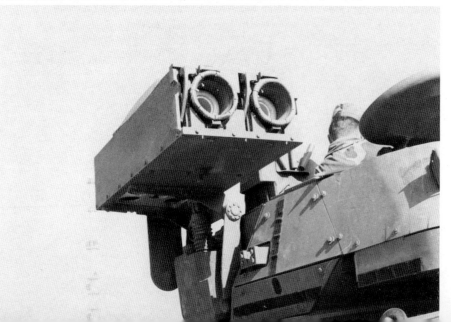

A Bradley fires a TOW missile round on the firing range. Early TOW missile rounds had a range of nearly two miles, while later improved TOW missiles have a greater range, shorter flight time and more powerful warheads. (FMC)

M2/M3 Turret

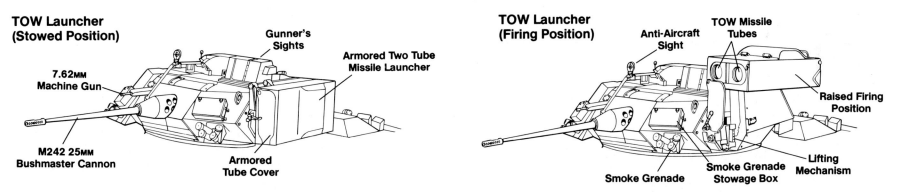

**TOW Launcher
(Stowed Position)**

Gunner's
Sights

Armored Two Tube
Missile Launcher

7.62MM
Machine Gun

M242 25MM
Bushmaster Cannon

Armored
Tube Cover

**TOW Launcher
(Firing Position)**

Anti-Aircraft
Sight

TOW Missile
Tubes

Raised Firing
Position

Lifting
Mechanism

Smoke Grenade
Stowage Box

Smoke Grenade

The rear of the turret has a stowage bin which runs completely around the rear of the turret. There are holes in the floor of the bin to allow water to drain out. Brackets are fitted to the rear of the stowage bin to carry addition 7.62 MM machine gun ammunition for the coaxial machine gun. (Jerchel)

The main external difference between the M2 and M3 are the firing ports mounted along the sides of the hull. On the M2 these ports carry the M231 FPW (a variant of the M16 rifle) which allows the infantry to fire their weapons while the M2 remains sealed against the threat of NBC warfare. (Jerchel)

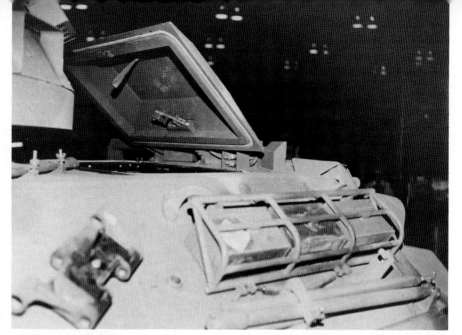

In addition to the rear ramp and hatch, the men in the rear compartment can also use the hatch on top of the compartment for observation, or egress in an emergency. The main function of this hatch is to allow crewmen to reload the two tube TOW launcher from a relatively protected position. (FMC)

On the M3 variant the firing ports are plated-over since the CFV is intended for scouting and cavalry type missions and carries a reduced infantry component of scouts. The two tube armored TOW missile launcher is in the retracted traveling position. (Mesko)

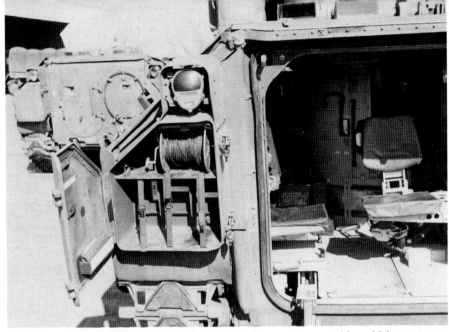

On the rear of either side of the hull, above the fenders, are stowage bins which can carry a variety of gear including ammunition, communications cable, rations and a stove. (Jerchel)

The driver's compartment of the Bradley is spacious and well laid out. The vehicle is controlled with the "butterfly" yoke positioned in the center of the instrument panel. All the switches are located within easy reach of the driver and the engine compartment is located to the right of the driver. (Army via Armor)

The driver is connected to the rear compartment by a narrow passageway. In the M2 variant two infantrymen are seated here and have two firing ports located along the side of the compartment. (FMC)

The main difference between the M2 and M3 was in the internal layout. The M2 troop compartment had seats for six infantrymen besides the three man crew. Four seats were in the rear and two more were in the crawl space to the driver's position. (FMC)

15

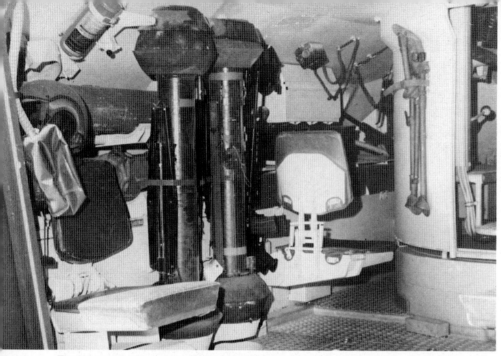

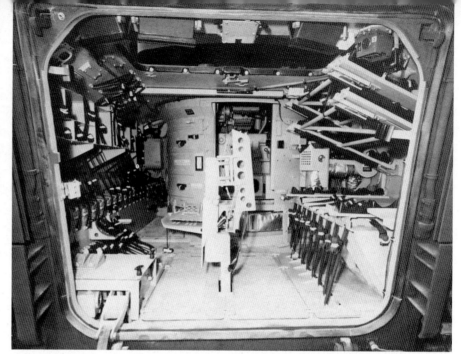

The M2 carries two portable TOW missile launchers for use by the infantry when dismounted. The vehicle had room for five stowed self-contained TOW rounds in the interior and five M72A2 LAW rocket launchers. (FMC)

Space within both variants was at a premium and ammunition was packed in every space large enough to hold an ammo box. On the right rear of the troop compartment, ammunition for the main gun, coaxial machine gun, and rifles are stowed and labeled. The circular objects (middle) are the firing ports for the troop weapons and the rectangular object above them are the sighting periscopes. (FMC)

In the M3 there were only two seats in the rear compartment for scouts, the extra space being taken up by additional ammunition storage and TOW rounds. The TOW rounds were stored in a folding rack (to the right) which was folded upward when not in use. (FMC)

The gunner sits to the left in the turret with a combined day/thermal image sight along with periscopes for front and side viewing. The gunners sight is located approximately in the center with his gun controls and firing trigger located just under it. (FMC)

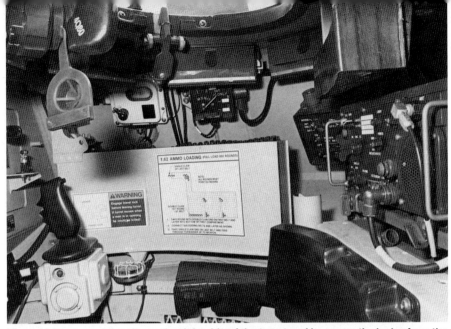

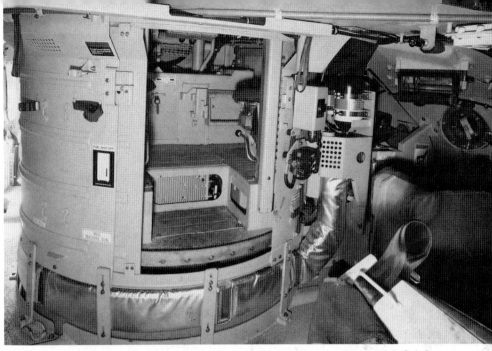

The vehicle commander sits on the right side of the turret and has an optical relay from the gunner's sight to his sight. In addition there is a backup sighting system in case of a failure of the primary system. Both men can fire the Bradley's various armament systems. (FMC)

The turret is mounted in a fixed receptacle which protrudes down into the vehicle's fighting compartment. The basic color of the interior is a Pale Green which is far less stark and easier on the eyes then the old Gloss White interiors used originally on the M113. (FMC)

By comparison with the vehicle it is replacing (the M113), the Bradley is a far superior vehicle in all respects. The Bradley is faster, better armed, and can do far more things then the M113, which first went into production nearly twenty-five years ago. (Jerchel)

The overall size of the Bradley, in this case an M3, is large due to all the capabilities installed in it. The height of the vehicle is evident when compared to the six foot soldier standing next to it. (Mesko)

The Bradley has a limited amphibious capability for crossing streams and rivers but cannot be used in open water (such as the ocean or a choppy lake). For river crossings the crew erects a swim barrier which is stored in the hull along the sides, rear and front. This vehicle was being tested at the FMC facility in California. (FMC)

The Bradley moves through water at a speed of about four and a half miles an hour using its tracks for propulsion. The weight of the engine on the right side tends to pull the vehicle in that direction and the crew must compensate for this tendency. The extremely low freeboard of the canvas swim screen means that the vehicle cannot ford any choppy water without being swamped. (FMC)

If the situation allows, the crew and infantry ride on top of the vehicle in case the Bradley is swamped. In training the crew it is also required to wear life preservers in case of an accident. The cable over the rear of the screen has been positioned so that if the vehicle does flounder, it can be more easily retrieved. (FMC)

There have been a number of accidents during training with the M2/M3 which have resulted in some loss of life. This particular Bradley was recovered after it sank during a training exercise at Fort Knox when the flotation screen collapsed. (FMC)

M2A1/M3A1

During 1986, FMC began production of an improved variant of the Bradley designated the M2A1/M3A1. This improved model was based on Research and Development (R & D) work carried out by FMC's Ground Systems Division, the Army Tank Automotive Command (TACOM), field reports and intelligence data.

The most significant improvement in the new variant was the installation of an improved TOW-2 missile system. The improved TOW had a large warhead, improved fuel, shorter flight time and better angle of attack. This newer, more power system was needed to combat the improved T64 and T72 series of Russian tanks which were coming into service and were capable of surviving hits from the older TOW system used on the M2/M3 series. While the earlier TOWs could handle the T55 and T62 models, the new Soviet MBT's had thicker, more advanced armor. The new TOW launcher has a slightly revised launcher cover, which has a rounded bottom edge.

In addition to the new TOW system, there were a number of external changes to the M2A1/M3A1. The rear turret stowage basket was redesigned, having a straight back instead of the slanted back used on the M2/M3. On the M3A1, the firing ports were deleted and replaced with solid armor on the sides and rear. The M3A1 also has a redesigned rear upper hatch with four periscopes (which replace the rear periscopes of the M2A1). The scout's seats were also relocated under the hatch to make it easier for the scouts to use them.

Other changes included the removal of the grenade ammunition boxes from the front of the turret, improved flotation screen brackets and an improved auto-interrupter to prevent the 25MM gun from damaging various hull fittings. The driver's hatch was modified, with a step guard being installed over the hatch periscopes to protect them.

Internally, a new NBC system was added, mounted in the turret bustle. This system allowed all the crew, along with the scouts in the M3A1, to breath filtered air through a hose rather than individual units. In the M2A1 the infantry squad was not provided with this option, since their constant movement in and out of the Bradley would mean numerous changes from one system to another, exposing them to needless danger.

The prototype M2E1 had additional periscopes mounted on the missile loader's hatch on the upper rear deck. (FMC)

The turret on the M2A1/M3A1 mounted a TOW-2 missile launcher. This launcher could be identified by the different shape of the missile launcher cover plate. The stowage boxes on the turret front were deleted and replaced by tie down straps. (B. Zaeske)

The differences between the M2/M3 and the next production variant, the M2A1/M3A1, were relatively minor. This vehicle served as the prototype under the designation M2E1. The vehicle was tested at Aberdeen Proving Grounds (APG). (APG via FMC)

The new upper missile loaders hatch has four periscopes in it for use by the crew. The installation of these periscopes led to the deletion of the periscopes from the rear deck of the M3A1. The color of the inside of the hatch is a Pale Green. (Mesko)

Turret Development

M2/M3

Grenade Stowage Box

Stowage Box

M2A1/M3A1

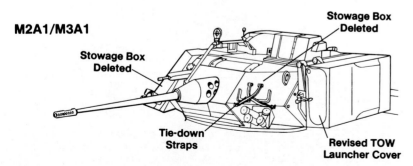

Stowage Box Deleted

Stowage Box Deleted

Tie-down Straps

Revised TOW Launcher Cover

The most noticeable external difference between the M2/M3 and M2A1/M3A1 is the redesigned stowage bin on the rear of the turret. The new bin has a straight back while the M2/M3 bin had a slanted back. In addition, the M3A1, has the firing ports deleted. The grenade stowage boxes on the turret front have also been deleted. This M3A1 Bradley is from the 11th Armored Cavalry Regiment, the Blackhorse Regiment. (Jerchel)

Another less obvious change is the addition of a step guard over the driver's periscopes, seen here on this M3A1 of the 11th ACR. (Jerchel)

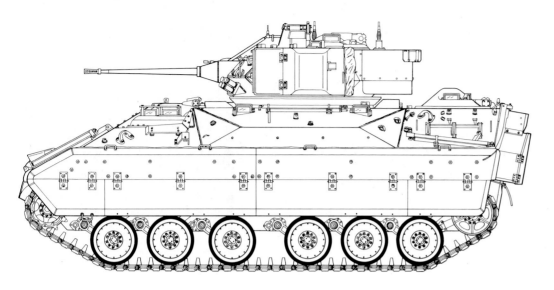

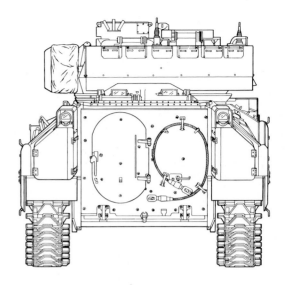

Specifications

M3A1 Bradley

Crew ....Three
Length ....21.5 feet
Width ....10.5 feet
Height ....9.75 feet
Weight ....60,000 pounds

Armament
Main ....25mm Bushmaster cannon
Secondary ....7.62mm coaxial machine gun
                            Improved TOW-2 missile launcher
Engine ....500 hp Cummins VTA 903 Diesel
Speed ....41 mph
Range ....300 miles

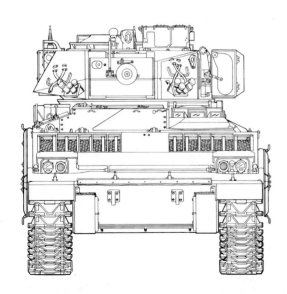

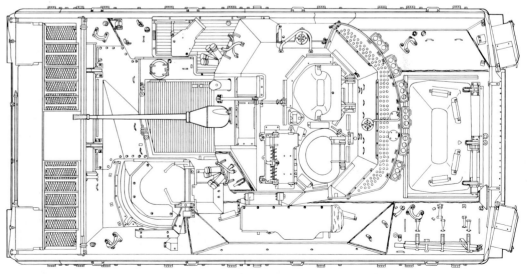

On the M3A1, the firing ports on the rear ramp have also been deleted since the troops onboard are not expected to have to fight from inside the vehicle, unlike the M2A1 crew. (Jerchel)

The driver of this M3A1 has a screen in front of him to help keep water and other road dirt from being thrown up into his face. The armored flaps over the gunner's sights are in the raised position. (Egon Merk)

An M3A1 of B Company, 4/7 Cavalry, 3rd Armored Division moves down a rain soaked German road during a NATO exercise. The M3A1 had the smoke grenade stowage boxes on the turret deleted and replaced with tie down straps. (B. Zaeske)

An M3A1 of the 11th Cav passes through a German village during a NATO exercise in September of 1989. The vehicle has a Yellow beacon light on the rear stowage box and a Tan tactical number on the turret. (Jerchel)

M2A2/M3A2

While the M2/M3 and M2A1/M3A1 were fairly well protected, advances in Soviet weapons technology soon outclassed their armor. Under new guidelines for increased protection against heavier caliber weapons, the Army and FMC began designing a new variant of the Bradley to withstand hits from these new Soviet weapons under the designations M2A2 and M3A2.

The original spaced laminated armor was replaced by two plates of one and one quarter inch steel armor that ran the length of the hull on both sides of the Bradley. While classified, observers believe this armor is sufficient to withstand hits up to 30MM cannon fire. In addition, reactive armor can also be fitted to increase survivability against shaped charge weapons. Armor plates have also been added to the front of the hull, eliminating the trim vane carried on the M2/M3 and M2A1/M3A1. The addition of this armor also led to a repositioning of the headlights on the hull front.

Armor plates were also added to the turret for increased protection. Additionally, the gun shroud around the 7.62 coaxial machine gun was deleted and a pair of smoke grenade stowage boxes were installed on the turret under the gun mantlet. These boxes were smaller and narrower than the stowage boxes used on the earlier M2/M3.

Internally, ammunition, mines and flares have been relocated to the lower and rear portions of the hull to reduce their exposure to enemy fire. Rigid Kevlar blankets, called spall liners, have also been fitted to the inside to stop armor spall, bullets and fragments from flying around the interior with devastating effects.

These armor and internal improvements have resulted in an increase in weight for the Bradley from 25 to 33 tons. To handle this thirty-two percent increase in weight, a new upgraded 600 horsepower Cummins engine was installed replacing the earlier 500 hp unit. The M2A2/M3A2 also has a regeared stronger transmission. Along with the new power plant and transmission, stronger torsion bars were added to the suspension to handle the increased weight. As a result of these modifications, the vehicles's performance has been somewhat decreased, although only slightly.

Production of the M2A2 and M3A2 began during the Spring of 1988, with the Army taking delivery of their first units that Fall. In 1989, Saudi Arabia placed an order for both variants of the Bradley, following an earlier demonstration of the Bradley in 1983. This was the first foreign order of the Bradley and as a result of the Gulf War, Saudi Arabia has increased their order.

While production of the M2A2/M3A2 continues, the Army has also planned to retrofit earlier M2A1s and M3A1s to the A2 standard. They will not modify the earlier M2s and M3s since the Army feels that such a move would not be cost effective, given the age and condition of the earlier vehicles.

In response to new weapons developed by the Russians, the Bradley was uparmored to improve its survivability on the battlefield. Additional one and one quarter inch armor plates were added to the hull front, sides and turret.

Hull Development

M2A1/M3A1

Trim Vane

Lights

M2A2/M3A2

Armor Plate

Repositioned Lights

Armored Engine Cover

Trim Vane Deleted

Armor Skirts

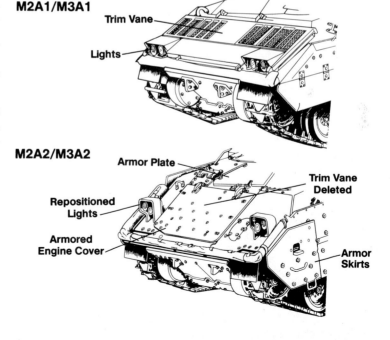

Armor plates have been bolted onto the hull and turret. The thickness of these armor plates can easily be gauged by looking at the sides of the turret where the plates overlap. (Mesko)

Turret Development

M2A1/M3A1

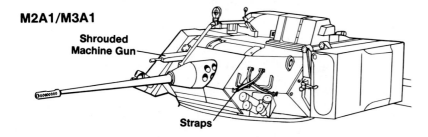

Shrouded Machine Gun

Straps

M2A2/M3A2

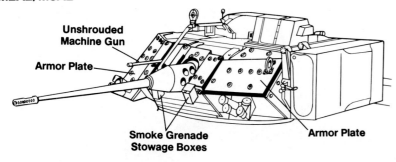

Unshrouded Machine Gun

Armor Plate

Smoke Grenade Stowage Boxes

Armor Plate

Whenever feasible, armor plates were added to flat surfaces on the Bradley, although such items as the TOW launcher and sighting devices were not uparmored due to their configuration and working mechanisms. The turret also had two grenade stowage boxes added to the gun mantlet. (Mesko)

The new armor plates also serve as attachment points for reactive armor tiles which are attached to the plates using these circular fittings. Reactive armor is explosive, sending out a countering explosion when hit by a shaped charge. (Mesko)

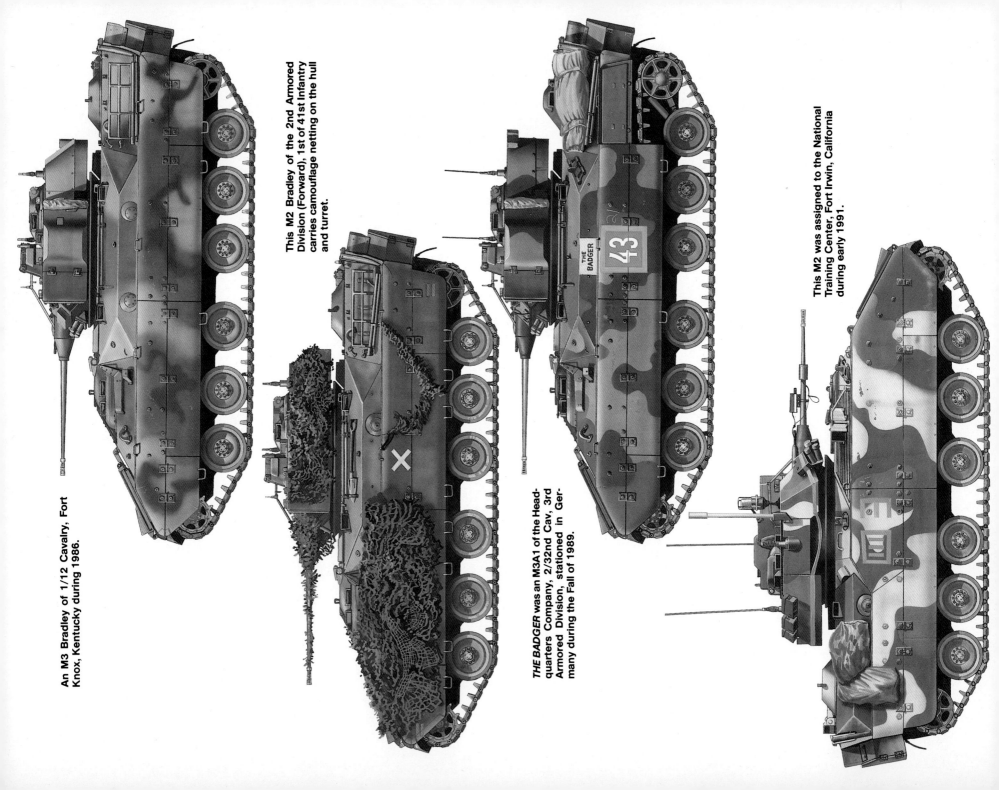

An M3 Bradley of 1/12 Cavalry, Fort Knox, Kentucky during 1986.

This M2 Bradley of the 2nd Armored Division (Forward), 1st of 41st Infantry carries camouflage netting on the hull and turret.

THE BADGER was an M3A1 of the Headquarters Company, 2/32nd Cav, 3rd Armored Division, stationed in Germany during the Fall of 1989.

This M2 was assigned to the National Training Center, Fort Irwin, California during early 1991.

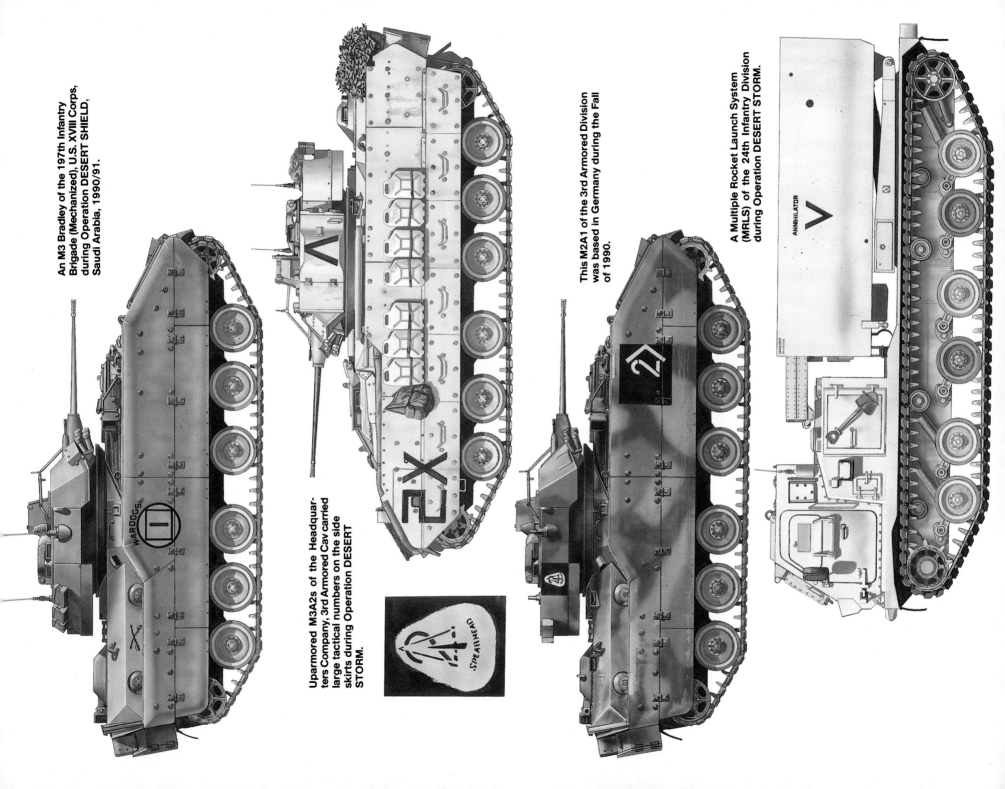

An M3 Bradley of the 197th Infantry Brigade (Mechanized), U.S. XVIII Corps, during Operation DESERT SHIELD, Saudi Arabia, 1990/91.

Uparmored M3A2s of the Headquarters Company, 3rd Armored Cav carried large tactical numbers on the side skirts during Operation DESERT STORM.

This M2A1 of the 3rd Armored Division was based in Germany during the Fall of 1990.

A Multiple Rocket Launch System (MRLS) of the 24th Infantry Division during Operation DESERT STORM.

The M3A2 was evaluated for use by the Royal Saudi Land Forces and an order for the vehicle was placed before the outbreak of Operation DESERT STORM. This particular vehicle was painted in a Sand camouflage and marked with a small Saudi insignia on the side armor for the evaluation. (FMC)

The weight of new armor has resulted in an upgrading of the engine to 600 HP, installation of a new transmission, improved floatation device and other minor changes. This M3A2 is out-fitted with the reactive armor tile. The addition of the new armor and other modifications has raised the combat weight of the Bradley from twenty-five tons to near thirty-three tons. (FMC)

This M3A2 of HQ Company, 1st Infantry Division reveals the unshrouded coaxial machine gun and extra armor plates installed on the turret. The two small boxes alongside the main gun are smoke grenade stowage boxes. (B. Zaeske)

27

An M3A2 of Headquarters Company, 16th Infantry, 1st Infantry Division moves forward during Centurion Shield '90. The crew has stowed extra gear on the engine cover and rear hull top. The vehicle carries a camouflage of Green, Brown and Black. (B. Zaeske)

A crewman rests on top of this Bradley of the HQ Company, 16th Infantry during Centurion Shield '90. The NATO exercise took place in Bavaria, Germany during January of 1990. The Yellow and Black tactical number on the vehicle side has been worn away. (B. Zaeske)

The driver of this M3A2 is standing in his hatch. The Black rubber-like object on the hull front and side is the swim screen. With the addition of the additional armor plating on the hull front, the trim vane found on the M2/M3 and M2A1/M3A1 was deleted. (B. Zaeske)

The extra armor on the M3A2 increased the vehicle's overall weight but did not impair its ability to operate on dirt roads or in cross-country operations. The vehicle's 500 hp engine was replaced by a 600 hp unit and the transmission was also improved. (B. Zaeske)

ADATS

With the demise of the SGT York anti-aircraft system in the Summer of 1985, the Army was left no viable air defense system for its armored units. A number of firms tendered bids to rectify this, including FMC (in conjunction with Martin Marretta and Oertitcon-Buhile of Switzerland). Basically, the Bradley chassis was mated with the Air Defense and Anti-Tank System (ADATS) developed by the U.S. and Swiss firms. The ADATS system consisted of a launch unit with eight missile tubes, four on each side of the central fire control module which housed various types of target acquisition units, including Infrared and TV.

The missiles can be used to destroy either aircraft or armor depending on the target selected by the operator inside the vehicle. Each rocket carries a twenty-six pound shaped charge warhead which has tremendous destructive capability. In tests, the missile has demonstrated the ability to penetrate upwards of 1,000MM of armor at high velocity. When used in the anti-aircraft mode, the warhead's steel fragmentation casing increases its chances of destroying the aircraft. Additionally, the unit was fitted with a 25MM cannon for the Forward Air Defense System - Line Of Sight - Forward - Heavy (FAADS-LOS-F-H) competition.

As part of this program, the Army purchased four Bradleys fitted with the ADATS. Aside from the deletion of internal fittings to accommodate the operators and their equipment, the ADATS Bradley remains similar to a standard unit, keeping maintenance in line with regular units. If the ADATS module and its weapons can perform as advertised, the system may be procured by the Army which has a requirement for close to 600 units. The breakup of the Soviet Union and severe budget cutbacks in Pentagon spending may restrict procurement or cancel this version of the Bradley.

When the SGT York anti-aircraft system was cancelled, the Army was left without a viable air defense system for its armored units. Numerous replacements have been proposed, including a Bradley outfitted with the ADATS system. The Bradley's turret was replaced with an ADATS turret that housed a radar unit, sensors, and eight missile tubes. (FMC)

A prototype Bradley/ADATS fires a missile during testing of the system. The 141 pound missile can be fired at both aerial and ground targets. Carrying a 26.5 pound warhead, the missile can penetrate up to 1,000 MM of armor at high velocity, while for aerial targets, the steel fragmentation casing gives the warhead a good probability of destroying or seriously damaging aircraft. (Jerchel)

For the American competition, the ADATS turret was also armed with a 25MM cannon on top of the missile housing. The cannon can be used for either ground or aerial targets. While the cannon increased the vehicle's weight, the overall height was not affected. (Oerlikan)

Future Bradleys

In order for any weapons system to be effective, it should constantly be upgraded in order to keep pace with new technology and advances in equipment by potential opponents. In the case of the Bradley, we have already seen how the M2/M3 needed to have its TOW system upgraded to keep pace with new Soviet Armor and how the M2A1/M3A1 received additional armor to enhance protection against newer weapons.

As part of this upgrading procedure, the Army in 1983 began a program known as the Combat Vehicle Armament System Technology (CVAST). This resulted in a new turret for the Bradley which mounted a 35MM Ares rapid-fire cannon. Tested in 1984, the new turret was not put into production since it was felt that the larger caliber gun was not needed. The system was kept on "hold" and is available should a situation arise that calls for an increase in Bradley fire power.

One of the most intriguing possibilities, not only for the Bradley but for armored vehicles in general, is the advances made in polymer composites and ceramic armor. These new materials may allow vehicles to be built using them in place of metals. This gives the vehicle a substantial weight reduction, enhanced crew survival since there would be little shrapnel if hit, reduced manufacturing cost and decreases in maintenance due to less corrosion and metal fatigue. The Bradley has already been fitted with such armor and the results have been encouraging, but at this point in time more developmental work needs to be done before such armor is practical for full scale production.

With the breakup of the Soviet Union, however, and the perceived view that the world is now at peace, future Bradley variants may never surface due to expense, Pentagon budget cutting and changes in U.S. foreign policy. While peace is indeed a prospect to look forward to, events in the Persian Gulf have shown that the world is still far from peaceful and hopefully the U.S. will keep abreast with new advances in order to provide its armed forces with effective weapons should they need to be deployed to some trouble spot far from home.

Though the current military situation does not seem to warrant production of this more powerful Bradley variant, tests have shown that the new turret and gun are practical and, should the need arise, it could be placed into production and used to upgrade earlier variants. (FMC)

Experiments have been conducted to see if the armor protection of the Bradley can be improved through the use of reinforced polymer composites and ceramics. It is hoped that the use of such materials can keep pace with the penetration power of newer weapons, while keeping down weight. In addition, such materials can reduce manufacturing cost, prolong vehicle life, and enhance crew survivability. (FMC)

In order to be ready should a potential enemy introduce new vehicles which the 25MM cannon could not handle, a new ARES 35MM Talon rapid-fire cannon was test fitted to a Bradley in a large two-man turret. These tests were conducted during 1983 under the Combat Vehicle Armament System Technology (CVAST) program. (FMC)

Close Combat Vehicle, Light (CCVL)

During the early 1980s the Army announced it was in the market for a new light tank to replace the M551 Sheridan and to equip American light, rapid deployment forces. In response to this requirement for an Armored Gun System (AGS), FMC submitted a light tank based on the Bradley and M113 components. The resulting vehicle was designated the Close Combat Vehicle, Light (CCVL) and looked much like a conventional tank.

The driver was located in the front, center portion of the hull, while the commander and gunner sit in tandem on the right side of the turret. The loader was eliminated through the use of an automatic loader which was designed by FMC's Northern Ordnance Division. This loader has a rate of fire of twelve rounds a minute and carries a variety of rounds.

The CCVL is fitted with a 105MM cannon and was fitted with similar sighting equipment to that used on the M1 Abrams Main Battle Tank, allowing the vehicle to engage targets under practically all battlefield and weather conditions. Using laminated armor of the type fitted to the Bradley, the CCVL can withstand hits up to 30MM over a 60 degree frontal arc, while the remaining hull portions can resist heavy machine gun fire. For additional protection, sixteen smoke grenade launchers are fitted on either side of the turret and a 7.62MM machine gun is mounted coaxially with the main gun. Power for the twenty ton vehicle is provided by a 575 hp Detroit Diesel Allison engine which gives the light tank a speed of 45 mph and a range of about 300 miles.

Overall dimensions and weight allow the CCVL to be carried and air dropped from the C-130, the smallest tactical transport in the U.S. inventory. With its hard hitting 105MM cannon, the CCVL is definitely one of the better vehicles now in competition for the AGS contract. Ironically, just prior to the deployment of American airborne forces to Kuwait, the CCVL prototype took part in tests at Fort Bragg against the Sheridan and a Marine Corps LAV-25. The Persian Gulf crisis underscored the need for such a vehicle and following the wars end, interest by the Army in the program remained strong. Unfortunately, the cutting of Pentagon budgets may doom procurement of any AGS, although events would seem to indicate the need for such a vehicle, particularly in light of a redefined U. S. foreign policy.

While this has been going on, FMC has been doing research on fitting the CCVL with

When the Army decided to seek a replacement for the M551 Sheridan for use by its airborne forces and light rapid deployment units, FMC developed the Close Combat Vehicle, Light (CCVL) using Bradley and M113 components. Armed with a 105MM cannon the lightly armored vehicle was capable of high speed and its overall dimensions made it relatively easy to conceal. (FMC)

reactive armor to enhance its survivability against weapons such as the RPG-7 rocket launcher, although care must be taken to keep within the parameters of weight and size so that it will remain air transportable. In addition. FMC is currently working on a new vehicle based on the CCVL for the export market under the designation VFM-5. Whether either vehicle will go into production is unknown, but this "Bradley" light tank is indeed a unique and interesting vehicle.

One of the key elements of the Army requirements was the ability for the new vehicle to be air transportable in a C-130, along with being capable of being parachuted into an area or delivered via the Low Altitude Parachute Extraction System (LAPES). These requirements allowed delivery of the vehicle to almost any battlefield where American forces may be committed. (US Army)

Using laminated armor (as in the Bradley) allows the CCVL to provide the crew with a certain degree of protection from light weapons and small arms, though it would not be able to withstand heavy armor piercing weapons. The vehicle has an FMC designed autoloader which has replaced the loader in the left side of the turret. The gunner and commander sit in tandem on the right side of the turret while the driver is located in the center front hull. (FMC)

M987 Fighting Vehicle System (FVS)

In order to support the new generation of M1 tanks and M2/M3 Bradleys, the Army issued a requirement for a new series of combat support vehicles which could keep up with these new AFVs. Using Bradley components, FMC developed the M987 Fighting Vehicle System. The Bradley components included the power train and suspension system in a chassis which is somewhat longer than the Bradley. The 500 horsepower engine is center mounted under the engine cab which can be tilted forward for easy access to the engine. Behind the cab/engine area is the payload area which can be used in a number of different configurations.

The cab provides seating for the driver and two additional personnel. Aluminum armor provides protection against various small caliber weapons and the cab is fitted with an overpressure ventilation system for operation in an NBC enviroment. Visibility through the front three windows is fairly good, and if under fire, folding shields can be lowered to protect the crew. Doors on each side have windows which can be covered with a hinged armor flap. The driving controls are logically placed and designed for easy use, while the instrument panel is labeled in international symbols and uses both English and metric units of measurement. An additional hatch in the roof allows for ventilation and observation when in a reasonably safe situation.

The M987 has been used as the basis for a number of vehicles with a wide range of functions. Some have been in service for some time, while others are still under development. The following are the current vehicles along with a short description of their function:

M933 Multiple Launch Rocket System (MLRS)

Initially known as the General Support Rocket System, this vehicle came about following a 1976 requirement issued by the Army for a vehicle to provide battlefield saturation fire using large caliber rockets. Competition for the contract was between Boeing and Vought, each developing their own specific system. The Army selected the Vought proposal, combining it with the FVS under the designation M933. A large, box-like container on the bed of the FVS houses twelve unguided nine inch (227MM) rockets which can be fitted with a variety of warheads. Housed within the container is a built-in derrick which is used to rapidly reload the unit using pallatized rounds. Reloading can be accomplished by a single crewman adding to the versatility of the system. The launcher can be elevated and traversed as needed for fire missions. The MLRS went into U.S. service in the mid-1980s and was also selected for use by Britain, Germany, Italy and the Netherlands. It was given its baptism of fire during the Persian Gulf War where it was used to provide heavy fire against Iraqi bunkers, tank concentrations, and other targets of opportunity.

Forward Area Armored Logistics System (FAALS)

This FVS variant was designed to give armored units a logistics vehicle which could operate in a forward battlefield situation. A large armored, box-like structure was mounted on the bed of the FVS which could carry either ammunition, fuel, or other necessary provisions needed to keep forward units supplied. A crane was built into the front right corner of the box to help unload the needed items directly to the vehicle being resupplied, cutting down on the exposure of both crews. Large hatches allow for speedy unloading, further cutting down on exposure to hostile fire.

Armored Maintenance Vehicle (AMV)

Similar in profile to the FAALS, the AMV was designed to allow maintenance to be done under fire in a hostile environment. The vehicle can change power plants, gun tubes and weapons stations with its 7.5 ton capacity crane which is fitted at the rear of the vehicle. Its large internal stowage area allows it to carry critically needed parts, repair materials and the tools needed to repair damaged AFVs in the forward battle area, thus reducing the need to retrieve these vehicles and transport them to the rear area. For self-defense, the vehicle is fitted with a .50 caliber machine gun mounted over the right side of the cab, along with smoke grenade launchers for concealment.

Electronic Fighting Vehicle System (EFVS)

In order to provide a mobile protective home for commanders with forward units, FMC developed the EFVS. This vehicle allows battlefield commanders to have access to

The Fighting Vehicle System (FVS) was designed using Bradley components to cut down on the costs of an entirely new armored logistical system. The FVS has the performance to keep up with the new generation of Army AFVs. The basic vehicle was constructed so that it could accept a number of different payloads for a variety of missions. The vehicle is somewhat longer than the standard Bradley but incorporates the same power train components and suspension. (FMC)

critical information and disseminate it as needed. FMC designed this vehicle to carry a wide variety of communications packages, electronic components and computers which allow the EFVS to function under fire while providing command, control, communications and intelligence on a timely basis for forward units. The module provides ballistic protection for the crew from small arms fire, artillery fragments, and incorporates an NBC over pressure protection system. In addition, armor kits are available for additional protection in high threat areas. It can operate totally closed up for up to two days with fuel resupply and has the ability to operate on the move using the primary power unit. To facilitate its mission, the unit is fitted with a remotely activated quick-erect mast at the rear which can be extended out to seventy feet.

Firefighter (Block III)

This variant was designed to use a Hughes phased array surveillance radar unit to detect enemy artillery, mortar and rocket positions and bring quick, rapid counter-battery fire upon their positions before they can move. The crew and their gear are protected against small arms fire and shrapnel in an armored module. The radar array is mounted on top of the module and is elevated as needed. When lowered the unit is only marginally higher then the similar shaped EFVS.

Long Range Anti-Tank Program (LRAT)

Developed in conjunction with Martin Marietta, this vehicle mounts elevated sensor systems designed to provide troops in the field with the ability to locate and identify distant targets. The vehicle uses a fifty foot telescoping mast linked to a Martin Marietta Target Acquisition and Designation System (TADS). Tests were also conducted to see if it was feasible to integrate the Hellfire missile system into the unit, to see if there was a potential for the vehicle to act as an infantry anti-tank unit which could destroy enemy armor while remaining under cover. Early results were encouraging, but as of yet no vehicles have been procured for service.

The Multiple Launched Rocket System (MLRS) carries a total of twelve nine inch (227mm) rockets in a large box which can be traversed and elevated. The unguided rockets have a range of some nineteen miles and can carry a variety of ammunition. This particular MLRS was one of the first to be received by the Army at FT Knox, Kentucky for troop orientation. (Mesko)

Fighting Vehicle System

M987 FVS
- Roof Hatch
- Forward Tilting Cab
- Payload Area
- Crew Door (Each Side)
- Modified Bradley Chassis/Suspension

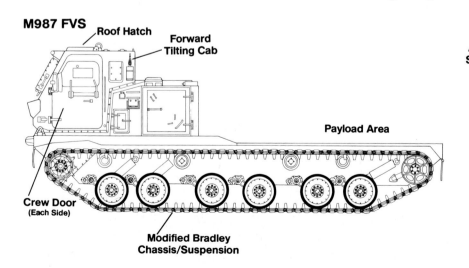

M933 MLRS (FVS Chassis)
- Armor Shields
- Derrick
- Trainable Armor Box For Twelve 9 inch Rockets

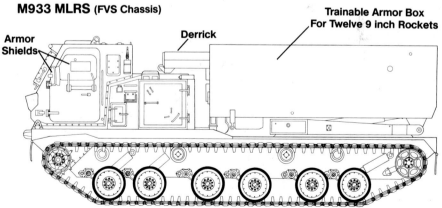

The twelve rocket canisters are arranged six on either side. The rockets can be fired singly, in groups or in salvo. The launcher traverse and elevation mechanism is visible under the launcher box. (Mesko)

The cab on the MLRS tilts forward for easy access to the engine. The cab is armored and provides the crew with protection against small caliber weapons and NBC threats through an over-pressurization system. The armored louvers in the front can be closed when firing or under fire. The driver's louvers fold onto the cab top, while the smaller two fold down. (Stewart)

The German Army also operates under the designation Medium Artillery Rocket System (MARS). One compartment is loaded with rockets while the second compartment is ready to reload a rocket pallet. The road objects are covers over the rocket containers to keep out dirt, moisture and other debris. (Roesner via Jerchel)

The reloading of the launcher can be accomplished in a short time with the built-in derrick which removes used rocket canisters and replaces them with a six round palletized container. This can be accomplished in a short period by a single crewman. (US Army/Vought via Armor)

An MLRS fires a rocket during early testing of the system. The lightweight cover over the container shatters when the rocket is fired. The rockets can be fired as singles, in pairs or in a quick sequence for saturation effect. During firing the armored louvers and door flaps are locked into position to protect the crew. (US Army via Armor)

To help keep forward armored units supplied with ammunition, food and fuel, FMC designed the Forward Area Armored Logistical System (FAALS) based on the FVS. Material is carried in the enclosed compartment and removed with a built-in crane. Access can also be gained through the large doors on either side of the vehicle. (FMC)

In the field the FAALS pulls up alongside the vehicle, in this case an M1, and gives the crew whatever they need from the cargo hold. This allows the armored units to keep up the pressure on the enemy with a minimum of loss of time to resupply. (FMC)

To maintain vehicles in the field, FMC developed the Armored Maintenance Vehicle (AMV) which carries spare parts and tools to undertake repair work. The vehicle has a crane at the rear which can lift up to seven and one-half tons. Equipped with welding gear, the AMV also has electric and hydraulic outlets which allows it to perform a variety of battlefield maintenance tasks. (FMC)

For spotting enemy firing positions for counter-battery fire, an FVS has been fitted with a Hughes phased-array surveillance radar system. This system allows the crew to locate enemy artillery, mortar and rocket positions so that counter-battery fire or air strikes can be directed against them while providing the crew with a certain amount of protection. (FMC)

In order to maintain control and evaluate the latest intelligence on the battlefield, FMC devised the Electronic Fighting Vehicle System (EFVS). Completely self-contained, the EFVS carries equipment for control, fire adjustment and secure communications. The armored module is over-pressurized and has an interlocking entrance to allow operations in an NBC environment. (FMC)

The radar antenna folds down on top of the module when not in use and for traveling. The armored louvers are also in the folded traveling positions: the drivers louvers fold upward, while the other two fold downward. (FMC)

This system was evaluated for use by infantry units as a possible anti-tank weapons system. Once the target was designated by a laser beam, missiles could be launched and directed to the target by the laser in much the same way as the Apache helicopter's Hellfire system. (FMC)

Work has also been carried out with elevated sensors to provide battlefield surveillance at long ranges for AFVs. In conjunction with Martin Marietta, FMC modified a standard FVS to carry a fifty foot elevating mast system, a Target Acquisition and Designation System designed by Martin and provision of a Hellfire missile launcher. (FMC)

Into Service

With its deployment into widespread use by the Army, the Bradley received its first real serious test as a combat system by the troops in the field — the most critical judges of any vehicle. For the most part, there were few serious complaints about the Bradley. The crew's liked it speed, handling characteristics and firepower. The Bradley was far and away the better vehicle when compared to the older M113. Its overall capabilities gave the troops a more versatile weapon which could perform a variety of tasks which the M113 could not handle. The Bradley's cannon and TOW system gave the troops a vehicle which could deal with any light AFVs encountered and even had a good chance to defeat enemy tanks under the right conditions.

As a result of the characteristics of the new Abrams and Bradleys, the Army re-organized its armored units and revised its tactics to utilize the speed, firepower and armored protection of these vehicles to the fullest. Training at stateside bases and in Europe resulted in new doctrines for tank/infantry employment. These new tactics were tested under simulated combat conditions at the National Training Center (NTC), Fort Irvine, California where units operated against the Corps of Opposing Forces (OPFOR) which were schooled in Soviet style tactics. This is the Army's equivalent of the Navy "Top Gun" or Air Force "Red Flag" programs. At the NTC, under the harsh desert sun, different tactics were tried as units trained under conditions very close to those of actual combat. This training would eventually serve the troops in good stead when events half-way around the world forced the United States to commit its forces to oppose un-provoked aggression.

Desert Storm

On 2 August 1990, Iraqi troops invaded the small, oil rich country of Kuwait. In a few short days Iraqi troops had total control of their smaller neighbor and the Iraqi dictator, Saddam Hussein, began making aggressive moves toward Saudi Arabia, the largest oil producing country in the Persian Gulf region. In response to this unprovoked attack and to forestall further moves by Hussein, American ground, naval and air units were rushed to the area.

Initially, only lightly equipped troops of the 82nd Airborne Division were deployed, equipped with the M551 Sheridan, basically a light tank/reconnaissance vehicle. These were followed a short time later by Marine Corps units which brought with them M60A1 Patton tanks, the first heavy armor the U.S. deployed to the region. By the end of August, however, elements of the 24th Infantry Division (Mechanized) began to arrive with their M1 Abrams MBTs and Bradleys. Despite this shown of resolve and various U.N. sanctions, Hussein refused to leave Kuwait. In fact, he showed increasing signs of belligerence as he moved additional armor and men into Kuwait and the southern Iraq region.

As a result of this, America increased its commitment by deploying additional forces, including nearly all of its armored and mechanized units from the U.S. and Europe. These included Bradley units from the 1st Cavalry, the 1st Infantry, the 1st, 2nd, and 3rd Armored (unless otherwise noted these denote divisions), the 197th Infantry Brigade and the 2nd and 3rd Armored Cavalry Regiments. These units deployed all three variants of the Bradley, while artillery units brought with them the MLRS (based on the Bradley).

While diplomats tried to find a peaceful solution to the crises, the various American units embarked on an extensive training program to acclimate their men and material to the harsh desert conditions. Extensive amounts of water were required for the men and soon every vehicle began carrying as much extra water as was practical. The fine, desert sand quickly got into every nook and cranny, resulting in more wear and tear on moving parts than was anticipated. This required an increase in preventive maintenance and a revamping of the lubrication schedules for vehicles. During this period of training, some problems arose with the Bradley, the most serious of which was the transmission in the A2 series which began to malfunction, causing the gears to lock in one position, basically disabling the vehicle. Trouble shooters from FMC and Army maintenance specialists eventually solved the problem in time for the vehicles to take part in the drive to free Kuwait. Other problems were relatively minor and resulted more from the desert environment than anything with the vehicle and were solved through careful maintenance and lubrication changes.

All this preparation became even more important when, after all diplomatic efforts had failed, the U.S. and its allies launched Operation DESERT STORM on 16 January 1991. For five weeks airpower blasted away at Iraqi positions in Kuwait and Iraq in preparation for the massive ground assault which everyone knew would follow.

After some minor actions, the main ground offensive began on 24 February. Using deception, the Coalition forces caught the Iraqis completely off guard. Elements of every major U.S. Armored unit rolled over position after position in one of the greatest military victories in history and the Bradley played a prominent role in this drive. Enemy resistance varied, although it was nowhere as heavy as earlier predicted. In conjunction with the Abrams, the Bradley ran roughshod over the Iraqi formations. Few Bradleys were lost to enemy action, and in fact more were damaged or destroyed by friendly fire during the confusion of battle.

By war's end, after a week of fighting, Bradleys were entering Kuwait and stood astride the only Iraqi escape route out of the city. The vehicle had performed exceedingly well in its first actual use in combat and crews were universal in their praise of the vehicle. Far from being the "Death-trap," which earlier newspaper accounts had labeled it, the Bradley did a creditable job, protected its crews and played a major part in the allied victory — no more could be asked of it.

Following formal Army acceptance of the Bradley, production moved ahead and in March of 1983, units at Fort Hood, Texas received their first M2s. In honor of the occasion, the new vehicle was fittingly introduced in a display at the base by the 1st Battalion, 41st Infantry Regiment, 2nd Armored Division. (FMC)

An M2A1 Bradley is unloaded at a staging area in Saudi Arabia. The vehicle was destined for use by the 1st Cavalry division. Hundreds of vehicles were shipped to the Gulf by sea while their crews flew in. (USAF)

Following the invasion of Kuwait in early August of 1990, the United States began to rush troops out to the Persian Gulf area to forestall a possible invasion of Saudi Arabia by Saddam Hussein. One of the first major Army ground units to deploy was the 24th Mechanized Infantry Division which was equipped with Bradleys. (USAF via Bishop)

While the Tan colored Bradleys blended in with the terrain, camouflage nets were used to provide additional concealment and a degree of shade for the crews and vehicles. (USAF via Bishop)

An interesting camouflage pattern that was tried by some units of the 24th Mechanized Infantry was broad bands of Gray outlined in what appeared to be Black. This scheme never caught on with other units and most Bradleys remained in an overall Sand color. (USAF)

Additional units arrived to bolster the initial American presence in the region, including elements of the 2nd Armored Division. This M2 from the 3rd Brigade of the 2nd Armored carries extra gear strapped to the hull prior to the crew moving out into the desert. The reverse chevrons were one variation of this type of marking used for vehicle recognition. (Army)

Some of the Bradleys which arrived in-country were still painted in their European type camouflage such as this vehicle of the 1st of the 3rd Cavalry. Due to the coating of sand and dust which most vehicles received in the desert, some units never bothered to paint their vehicles as they felt it was a waste of time. (USAF via Cole)

44

A platoon of Bradleys come together in the desert for general maintenance and to lager in for the night. They have backed into position and each vehicle covers one sector for an all-round defensive perimeter. This makes it easier to guard against a surprise attack from any quarter. (Army)

The crews of this Bradley platoon relax at a rear area camp. The folding chair next to the nearest Bradley has a hole in the seat, probably for use as a portable toilet in the field. These Bradleys are loaded with a wide variety of gear used to make their stay in the field more comfortable. (Army)

In the Fall, additional reinforcements arrived to supplement the U.S. and Allied contigents already in place. Included in these reinforcements were M2A2s and M3A2s fitted with additional armor. This M2A2 was being unloaded at a Saudi dock after sea shipment from the U.S. (USAF via Cole)

In addition to the Bradley, the MLRS was also deployed to support American troops in the region. Early arrivals, such as this vehicle, came in the older four-tone camouflage scheme which was in the process of being changed over to a new three-tone version at the time they were deployed. (Army via Bishop)

Most, if not all of the MLRS vehicles received a coat of camouflage paint which helped them to blend in with the desert sand. This MLRS of the 24th Division prepares to take part in a training exercise prior to the commencement of hostilities. (Army)

An MRLS of the 24th Infantry Division takes up position in the desert. The MRLS was widely used to counter Iraqi artillery which had a longer range than some of the Allied field pieces. (Army)

An M3 Bradley of the 24th Infantry Division halts during a patrol of the Saudi desert. The chevron and vehicle number were in Gray. The Gray edged in Black camouflage was unique to Bradleys of the 24th Infantry. (Army)

Much like their predecessors in other conflicts, the American troops carried everything they thought they might need strapped to their Bradleys. A wide variety of gear is visible on this vehicle as one of the crew relaxes on the front of the vehicle and reads a book. (Army)

Prior to the outbreak of the ground war the troops added names, graffiti and unit insignias to their vehicles to help break up the boredom. The name on this Bradley *AND HELL WILL FOLLOW*, perhaps sums up best what happened to Saddam Hussein's forces when the Iraqi dictator refused to withdraw from Kuwait. (Army)

An M3 Bradley of the 197th Infantry Brigade (Mechanized), XVIII Corps moves out from base camp in the Saudi desert during Operation DESERT STORM. The unit's Bradleys were active during the push into Kuwait. (Army)

This 3rd Armored Cav Bradley is loaded down with extra water containers on the side skirts. Crews who returned from DESERT STORM knew the value of having extra water while operating in the desert, either in Saudi Arabia or at the NTC. (Army)

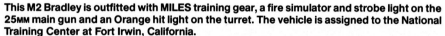

This M2 Bradley is outfitted with MILES training gear, a fire simulator and strobe light on the 25MM main gun and an Orange hit light on the turret. The vehicle is assigned to the National Training Center at Fort Irwin, California.

A couple of Bradleys during a break in training at the NTC. The ability of U.S. troops to load their vehicles with all sorts of extra gear is astounding. The difference between the early and late turret stowage rack allows the crews to carry more gear under some cover. (Stewart)

This M3A2 Bradley was part of a training exercise at the NTC after Operation DESERT STORM. The lessons learned in this war were quickly passed on to other units via the training exercises held at the NTC. (Stewart)

Soldiers from the 3rd Armored Cav who fought against the Iraqi's, redeployed stateside and participated in training exercises at the NTC where they passed on their knowledge to the cadre at the center. These Bradleys carry a wide variety of tactical markings on the hull. (Stewart)

US Armor in action

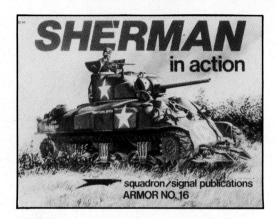

2016

2023

2025

2026

2028

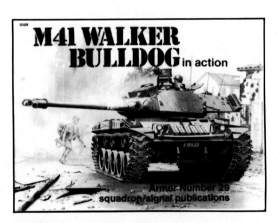

2029

 **squadron/signal publications**